The Presidential Range
Its Geologic History and Plate Tectonics

J. Dykstra Eusden

Department of Geology
Bates College
Lewiston, Maine 04240

deusden@bates.edu

Durand Press
Lyme, New Hampshire 03768
www.durandpress.com

Published by Durand Press,
25 Lamphire Hill Lane
Lyme, New Hampshire
03768
www.durandpress.com
Printed in the U.S.A.

ISBN: 978-0-9708324-6-7

All photographs are by the author.

Grant support for the project was from Bates College, the National Science Foundation, the New Hampshire Geological Survey, the Petroleum Research Fund of the American Chemical Society, and the United States Geological Survey EdMap and StateMap Programs

Table of Contents

The Yardstick of Geologic Time

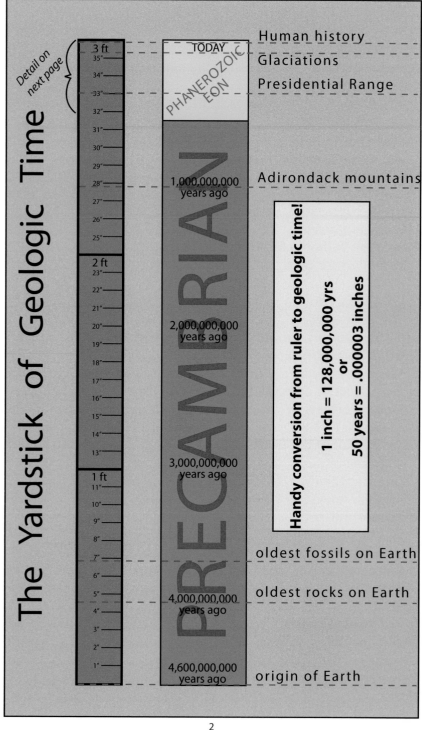

Detail on next page

3 ft		TODAY	Human history
35"			Glaciations
34"		PHANEROZOIC EON	
33"			Presidential Range
32"			
31"			
30"			
29"			
28"		1,000,000,000 years ago	Adirondack mountains
27"			
26"			
25"			
2 ft			
23"			
22"			
21"			
20"		2,000,000,000 years ago	
19"			
18"			
17"			
16"			
15"			
14"			
13"			
1 ft			
11"		3,000,000,000 years ago	
10"			
9"			
8"			
7"			oldest fossils on Earth
6"			
5"			oldest rocks on Earth
4"		4,000,000,000 years ago	
3"			
2"			
1"		4,600,000,000 years ago	origin of Earth

PRECAMBRIAN

Handy conversion from ruler to geologic time!

1 inch = 128,000,000 yrs
or
50 years = .000003 inches

Geo-events in the Presidential Range

3 ft		Quaternary	Glaciations	
		1,800,000 years ago		
	EON	CENOZOIC ERA		
		Tertiary		
35"		65,000,000 years ago		Long period of erosion no exposed rocks of this age
		MESOZOIC ERA		
		Cretaceous		
		144,000,000 years ago		
		Jurassic	Basalt intrusions and fracturing	
34"		206,000,000 years ago		
	PHANEROZOIC	Triassic		Long period of erosion no exposed rocks of this age
		250,000,000 years ago		
		Permian		
		300,000,000 years ago		
		Carboniferous		
33"		354,000,000 years ago	D5 and D4 folding metamorphism & granites	Acadian Orogeny
		Devonian	D3 folding, D2 faulting max metamorphism	
			metamorphism & granites D0 faulting, D1 folding	
		412,000,000 years ago	End of sedimentation	
		Silurian	Beginning of sedimentation	
		439,000,000 years ago		
32"		Ordovician	Taconic Orogeny, volcanism, oldest rocks	
		510,000,000 years ago		
		Cambrian		
		540,000,000 years ago		

Youngest Part of the Yardstick of Geologic Time

PALEOZOIC ERA

Is it really the "Granite State"?

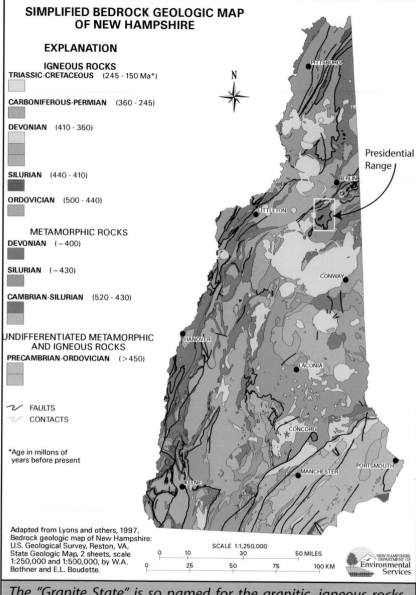

**SIMPLIFIED BEDROCK GEOLOGIC MAP
OF NEW HAMPSHIRE**

EXPLANATION

IGNEOUS ROCKS

TRIASSIC-CRETACEOUS   (245 - 150 Ma*)

CARBONIFEROUS-PERMIAN   (360 - 245)

DEVONIAN   (410 - 360)

SILURIAN   (440 - 410)

ORDOVICIAN   (500 - 440)

METAMORPHIC ROCKS

DEVONIAN   (~400)

SILURIAN   (~430)

CAMBRIAN-SILURIAN   (520 - 430)

**UNDIFFERENTIATED METAMORPHIC
AND IGNEOUS ROCKS**

PRECAMBRIAN-ORDOVICIAN   (>450)

⌇ FAULTS
⌇ CONTACTS

*Age in millons of
years before present

Presidential Range

PITTSBURG
BERLIN
LITTLETON
CONWAY
HANOVER
LACONIA
CONCORD
PORTSMOUTH
MANCHESTER
KEENE

N

Adapted from Lyons and others, 1997,
Bedrock geologic map of New Hampshire:
U.S. Geological Survey, Reston, VA,
State Geologic Map, 2 sheets, scale
1:250,000 and 1:500,000, by W.A.
Bothner and E.L. Boudette.

SCALE 1:1,250,000

0   10   30   50 MILES

0   25   50   75   100 KM

NEW HAMPSHIRE
DEPARTMENT OF
Environmental
Services

*The "Granite State" is so named for the granitic, igneous rocks
shown on the map in yellow, pink, red, and orange. But, there
are just as many metamorphic rocks shown in the blue, green
and purple, and the highest peaks, the Presidential Range, are all
metamorphic schists. The "Schist State" instead?*

Introduction

This guide and its accompanying geologic map of the Presidential Range are the results of bedrock mapping done by geologists at an unusually detailed scale (1:3,000) from 1990 to 2009. The resulting map significantly updates and improves any previous maps. This guide includes a description of the plate tectonic history of the Presidential Range, radioactive age dating done to determine the ages of granites and the metamorphism, and the field localities where representative rock outcrops can be observed. The most significant part of this guide is the detailed map that may be used by geology enthusiasts to explore the bedrock at their own pace while in the mountains or at home.

Generations of geologists have studied the rocks in the Presidentials in an effort to unravel the complicated story about former oceanic sediments that were deformed by folding and faulting. These rocks were finally metamorphosed to become the mica-rich schists and rugged quartzites of the Presidentials today. Collectively, this geologic research is getting us ever closer to an accurate plate tectonic model for the mountains; the theory of which simply states that the Earth's outer shell is composed of brittle plates that collide to produce lofty mountains and separate to produce new oceans. Mountains and oceans are dynamic features on the Earth, constantly moving, but at such slow geologic rates that the bedrock seems static and fixed to us. Deciphering the ancient plate tectonic configuration of an old eroded mountain belt like the Presidentials has proven to be extremely difficult for geologists. As a result there are many different plate models proposed, all of which might work.

Geologic maps and cross sections represent the canvas upon which a geologist portrays the rocks examined in the field. The maps show the bird's eye view of the rock units as if there was no water bodies, soil, or vegetation covering them. The cross sections give the vertical perspective. To visualize a cross section, picture making a deep slice into the Earth with a giant's knife, removing one side of the rocks, and looking at the vertical cliff you've just exposed; a cross section is born! These cross sections

5

extend deep into the Earth's crust going to depths of several thousand feet.

The guide is not designed as a trail map nor a guide to hiking in the Presidential Range. Use extreme care when examining outcrops of rocks shown in this guide. Some are in steep gullies, in rivers, or in remote locations far from trails. Many are in the alpine zone where off-trail hiking that damages fragile alpine ecosystems is discouraged. Trail maps and route descriptions are available through the Randolph and Appalachian Mountain Clubs.

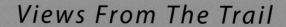

Views From The Trail

Panoramic view of the northern Presidential Range from Chandler Ridge. The peaks from left to right are, Mt. Jefferson in the shade, Mt. Adams in full sun, and Mt. Madison in partial shade.

View looking south toward Mt. Monroe from the summit cone of Mt. Washington on a fall day with alpine grasses in peak foliage and a rare cloud undercast.

Tectonic History

The tectonic history of the Presidential Range begins about 450 million years ago. The geologic time scale on pages 2 and 3 show the timing of the main geologic events and the ages of the rocks in the range. To visualize the movement of tectonic plates, land masses, and oceans over time, Chris Scotese of the PALEOMAP project has made a series of global maps. He determined the positions of the plates by measuring the ancient magnetic field locked in magnetic minerals in the rocks. This information yields the paleo-latitude on the globe, but little on the paleo-longitude. For example, from his work we know that much of the plate collisions that formed the Presidential Range occurred south of the equator, but we are not as sure about which lines of longitude the colliding plates were located .

On the following paleogeographic illustrations continental plates are shown as olive-green landmasses and include shallow marine platforms. Ocean plates are shown in darker shades of blue in the deep basins of the oceans. Spreading ridges in the oceanic crust are shown with a single line and two arrows pointing in opposite directions. These arrows indicate the direction that newly formed ocean crust moves away from the ridge. Oceanic plates descend beneath continental plates in regions of collision. These trenches or subduction zones are shown with an orange line with teeth. The teeth rest on the plate that does not subduct. These subduction boundaries are analogous to the modern tectonic setting in the Pacific Northwest where the Pacific oceanic plate is subducting beneath the west coast of the North American continental plate producing volcanoes such as Mt. St. Helens, Mt. Rainier, and Mt. Shasta.

The names of the old oceans and former plates are indicated on the maps. For example, the closure of the Iapetus Ocean occurred when the Avalonian plate collided with the Laurentian plate forming the Appalachian mountains. Usually there is some familiar modern boundary on the map like the present Atlantic coastline in New England or the Great Lakes shoreline. These lines provide a frame of reference over geologic time but, of course, would not even be in existence hundreds of millions of years ago. They are intended to help us see where things are on the map.

Building Vermont

The Green and Taconic mountains of Vermont initially developed when the large continental plate of Laurentia collided with at least two smaller volcanic arcs in the Iapetus Ocean: the Shelburne Falls arc, and farther to the east, the Bronson Hill arc. Each of these small plates consisted of a string of active volcanic islands, called an island arc, much like the present Aleutians Islands in Alaska. The volcanic arcs were separated from each other and Laurentia by two oceans, named the West and East Iapetus oceans. The Greek mythological connection in naming

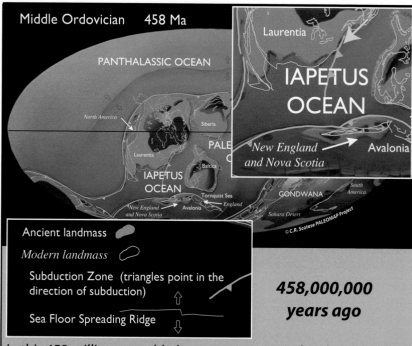

Middle Ordovician   458 Ma

PANTHALASSIC OCEAN

Laurentia

IAPETUS OCEAN

New England and Nova Scotia → Avalonia

North America
Siberia
Laurentia
Baltica
IAPETUS OCEAN
Tornquist Sea
England
GONDWANA
South America
New England and Nova Scotia → Avalonia
Sahara Desert

© C.R. Scotese PALEOMAP Project

Ancient landmass

Modern landmass

Subduction Zone (triangles point in the direction of subduction)

Sea Floor Spreading Ridge

458,000,000 years ago

In this 458 million year old plate reconstruction, the plates involved in the collision that formed the Appalachians are Laurentia and Avalonia. The Iapetus ocean separated these and was closing as at least two subduction zones gobbled its ocean crust. One of these subduction zones had a volcanic arc associated with it and formed the Ordovician Ammonoosuc Volcanics and Oliverian gneisses seen on the accompanying geologic map. The yellow arrow shows where the arc was erupting. Note, this happened south of the equator.

the oceans is that Iapetus was the father of Atlas for whom the present Atlantic Ocean is named.

All of this was happening during the Cambrian and Ordovician geologic time periods, approximately 540 to 450 million years ago. These ages are well constrained by fossils and many radioactive age dates determined in university and government geochronology labs across North America. The main collision took place in the Middle Ordovician, approximately 460 million years ago as both oceans closed and the arcs collided with Laurentia producing the Vermont mountains. These arc collisions are collectively called the Taconic Orogeny. The global-plate setting at this time can be seen in the 458 Million year old map. Slivers of the Iapetus Ocean crust were thrust up onto Laurentia during this plate collision and are now exposed throughout Vermont, Quebec, and Maine. The net effect was that North America gained some real estate in the form of two small volcanic arcs, the Bronson Hill and Shelburne Falls arcs, and the Middle Ordovician coastline pushed east, approximately to the present day Vermont-New Hampshire border.

In the Presidential Range there are only a few exposures that are a product of this orogeny. All of these are along the lower elevation flank of the northern part of the Presidential Range near the Town of Randolph, New Hampshire. Beautiful outcrops in the waterfalls of both Snyder and Cold Brooks expose the old Ammonoosuc volcanic rocks of the Bronson Hill arc.

Building the Presidential Range

During the Taconic Orogeny, the majority of the rocks that make up the Presidential Range did not exist. Their history begins with the next global map. Approximately 425 million years ago, two other oceans existed in this part of the world. The Kronos Ocean separated the composite and large Laurentia/Shelburne Falls/Bronson Hill plate from a plate called Avalon. The Rheic Ocean separated Avalon from the Gondwana plate. Geologists think Avalon was a long narrow plate, only 100 to 200 kilometers in width, but one thousand kilometers long, not unlike the present size and shape of New Zealand. Gondwana was similar in size to the African plate.

During the Silurian and Devonian geologic time periods, approximately 430 to 410 million years ago, great volumes of sediment were shed from adjacent eroding

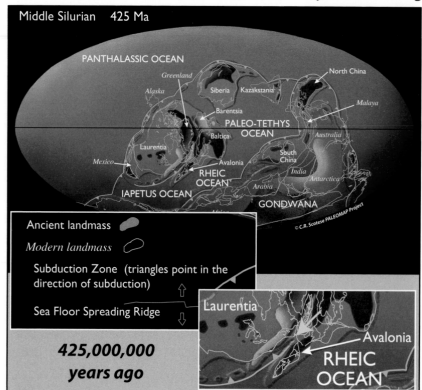

Middle Silurian   425 Ma

425,000,000 years ago

The map above shows that 425 million years ago, the Kronos Ocean existed between Avalonia and Laurentia. Its location is shown by the yellow arrow on the map. Great volumes of sediment from both Laurentia and Avalon were shed into the ocean becoming the sedimentary rocks that ulitmately formed the Presidential Range. The rocks on the map that correspond to these sediments are the Silurian Rangeley, Perry Mountain, Smalls Falls, and Madrid Formations and the Devonian Littleton Formation. The total thickness of sediment dumped into the Kronos Ocean was between 10 and 15 kilometers. The Kronos was rapidly closing along a subduction zone, perhaps two, and all of this tectonic action was happening south of the equator.

mountains into the Kronos and Rheic Oceans. Imagine that right after the Vermont mountains formed, those high peaks, perhaps as tall as the present Andes, were attacked by weathering, rain, and glaciers. They rapidly eroded and lost their height. The sediments derived from these eroding mountains made their way to the Kronos Ocean via ancient, now extinct river systems and were deposited both near shore and out into the deep marine basin of the Kronos.

The Kronos Ocean sediments became the rocks that can now be seen as one hikes through the Presidential Range. Throughout the Range you can see vestiges of the ancient sedimentary layering or bedding. These former sedimentary rocks are now the folded metamorphic rocks, transformed during the main plate collision between Laurentia and Avalon.

The Acadian Collision

The Acadian Orogeny created the Presidential Range in the Early Devonian when the continental plate of Avalon collided with the Laurentia/Shelburne Falls/Bronson Hill plate. The oceanic sediments caught between the two plates were deformed and metamorphosed to make the Presidential Range. People often ask geologists how tall these peaks were. Our best estimate is that they were comparable to the present Rockies or roughly 15,000 feet tall, but not as tall as the Himalayas.

One interesting aspect of this story is the lack of consensus on possible plate tectonic configurations for the Acadian Orogeny. Geologists have different views on the direction of subduction and the number of plates involved in the collision. This is largely because the rocks necessary to figure it all out are not exposed. For example, there are no volcanic arc rocks, slices of oceanic crust, or any other evidence besides the sediments to work with. A relatively new development in Appalachian plate tectonic theory has a microcontinent called Gander forming the basement of the Presidential Range. The Acadian collision of Avalon would still provide the stresses that made the mountains but Gander would have been caught between it and Laurentia.

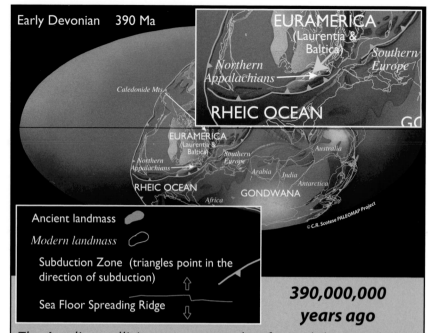

Early Devonian   390 Ma

EURAMERICA
(Laurentia & Baltica)

Southern Europe

Northern Appalachians

Caledonide Mts.

RHEIC OCEAN

GC

EURAMERICA
(Laurentia & Baltica)

Southern Europe

Australia

Northern Appalachians

Arabia   India

Antarctica

RHEIC OCEAN

GONDWANA

Africa

© C.R. Scotese PALEOMAP Project

Ancient landmass

Modern landmass

Subduction Zone (triangles point in the direction of subduction)

Sea Floor Spreading Ridge

390,000,000 years ago

The Acadian collision or orogeny that formed the Presidential Range (yellow arrow on map) happened in the Early Devonian. The Kronos Ocean closed completely and the mountains grew in height. After years of acquiring radioactive age dates on the rocks, geologists have been able to constrain the age of collision across New England. It is clear now that the collision began along the Maine coastline 420 million years ago and marched progressively northwestward across Maine, New Hampshire, and finally into Quebec. Based upon a radioactive age date in the Great Gulf on rocks at Wamsutta Falls, the northwest migrating mountain front "hit" the Presidential Range 408 million years ago during the early Devonian time period. At that time, the Presidential Range was just beginning to grow, and to the southeast towards Maine loomed already formed and still growing mountains. Northwest of the Presidential Range was a rapidly shrinking ocean, the last gasp of the Kronos, which extended into western New Hampshire and portions of Vermont and Quebec. You could have stood on the brand-new Mt. Washington and looked west across an ocean which covered the present towns of Littleton and Whitefield. Behind you would have been an extensive mountain range the size of the Rocky Mountains.

Pangea Forms

      The final collision in the history of the Appalachians is shown in the next two global maps. Here the Laurentia/ Shelburne Falls/Bronson Hill/Avalon continental plate collided with the Gondwana plate closing the Rheic Ocean. Some of the mountains that formed 320-270 million years ago during the Late Carboniferous Alleghenian Orogeny make up the valleys and ridges of Pennsylvania. No significant mountains formed in New England during this time.

The Atlantic Ocean Opens

      Once the collisional tectonic episodes finished culminating in Pangea, the Earth's restless plates started to extend, splitting Pangea and creating the Atlantic Ocean. This began about 180 million years ago in the Triassic geologic period. Today the Atlantic is still getting wider, at the same rate your fingernails grow (2-5 cm per year). During this period of crustal splitting, there was

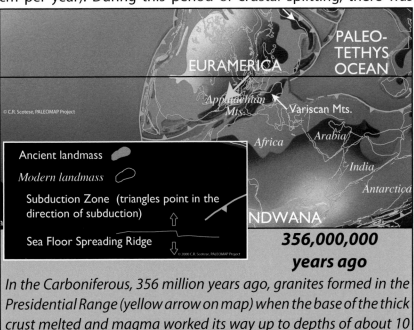

PALEO-TETHYS OCEAN

EURAMERICA

© C.R. Scotese, PALEOMAP Project

Appalachian Mts.

Variscan Mts.

Africa

Arabia

India

Antarctica

NDWANA

Ancient landmass

Modern landmass

Subduction Zone (triangles point in the direction of subduction)

Sea Floor Spreading Ridge

© 2000 C.R. Scotese, PALEOMAP Project

356,000,000 years ago

In the Carboniferous, 356 million years ago, granites formed in the Presidential Range (yellow arrow on map) when the base of the thick crust melted and magma worked its way up to depths of about 10 kilometers and solidified into granites. Gondwana and Euramerica continued on a collision course as the Rheic Ocean shrank.

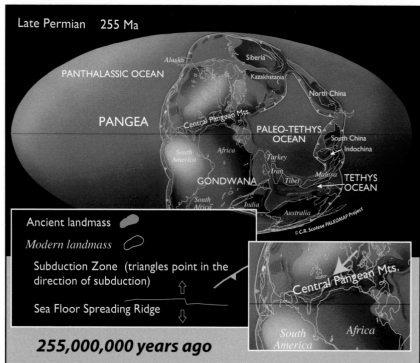

Late Permian   255 Ma

PANTHALASSIC OCEAN

Alaska

Siberia

Kazakhstania

North China

PANGEA

Central Pangean Mts.

PALEO-TETHYS
OCEAN

South China

Indochina

South
America

Africa

Turkey

Iran

Tibet

Malaya

GONDWANA

TETHYS
OCEAN

South
Africa

India

Australia

© C.R. Scotese PALEOMAP Project

Ancient landmass

Modern landmass

Subduction Zone (triangles point in the
direction of subduction)

Sea Floor Spreading Ridge

Central Pangean Mts.

South
America

Africa

255,000,000 years ago

Pangea formed when Laurentia and Gondwana came together as a single plate; a super-continent where one could walk uninterrupted by oceans from California to Australia. The now eroding mountains of the Appalachians are shown on the map as the Central Pangean Mountains. The yellow arrow marks the approximate location of the Presidential Range, now located in the northern hemisphere. A few regions of African rocks are found in Nova Scotia, left behind after Pangea split apart. These Canadian rocks match those found in Morocco.

a great deal of volcanism in New Hampshire. You can see these rocks in Franconia Notch, the Pemigewassett Wilderness and on Cathedral Ledge in Conway. However, in the Presidential Range, only a few rocks of this age exist in the form of narrow, meter-wide basalt dikes scattered throughout the range, and rare volcanics in Pinkham Notch. Two of the best places to see basalt dikes in the Range are in Tuckerman Ravine where the trail deflects around the headwall waterfall and in Pinnacle Gully in Huntington Ravine; a trailess route often ascended by ice and rock climbers.

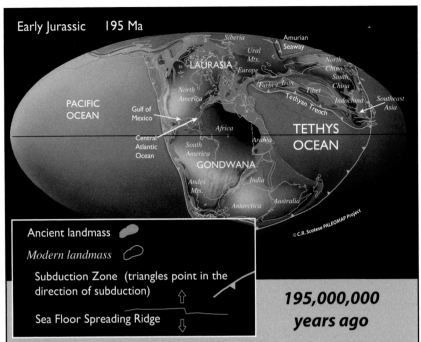

Early Jurassic   195 Ma

Siberia
Amurian Seaway
Ural Mts.
LAURASIA
Europe
North China
South China
Turkey Iran
Tibet
Tethyan Trench
Indochina
Southeast Asia
North America
PACIFIC OCEAN
Gulf of Mexico
Africa
Arabia
TETHYS OCEAN
Central Atlantic Ocean
South America
GONDWANA
Andes Mts.
India
Antarctica
Australia

© C.R. Scotese PALEOMAP Project

Ancient landmass

Modern landmass

Subduction Zone (triangles point in the direction of subduction)

Sea Floor Spreading Ridge

195,000,000 years ago

In the Triassic and Jurassic periods, Pangea rifted and the new Atlantic Ocean was born. Very few rocks recording this event are found in the Presidential Range with the exception of thin, meter wide basalt dikes scattered here and there. The ocean continues to widen today at 2-5 cm per year. Millions of years from now the Atlantic ocean will eventually close and new mountains will form.

Plate tectonic cross sections in the Presidential Range

470 million years ago: Pre-Taconic Orogeny

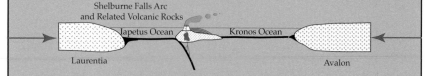

450 million years ago: End of Taconic Orogeny and formation of the Bronson Hill Arc

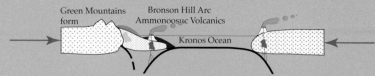

420 million years ago: Silurian and Devonian marine deposition

410 million years ago: Beginning of the Acadian Orogeny in the Early Devonian

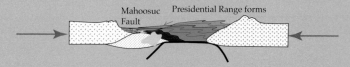

360 million years ago: End of the Acadian Orogeny, rise of the Jefferson Dome, and intrusion of Carboniferous granites

180 million years ago: Opening of the Atlantic Ocean and intrusion of basalt dikes in the Mesozoic

The Geologic Map

The map in the back pocket shows the surface distribution of rock types in the Presidential Range of New Hampshire's White Mountains. Most of the rocks are metamorphic in origin, having been recrystallized from older sedimentary and less abundant volcanic rocks. A few rocks are igneous, having been formed by the crystallization of magma as it cooled. The forest and soil that cover the rocks are not shown so that the underlying bedrock can be inferred. Each rock type is given a name and assigned a corresponding abbreviation and color that are keyed to the legend which also contains detailed descriptions of the age, texture, color, mineralogy, and thickness of each map unit. For example, the "Src" labeled on the map refers to the Silurian Crawford Member of the Rangeley Formation while "Oama" represents the Ordovician amphibolite member of the Ammonoosuc Volcanics.

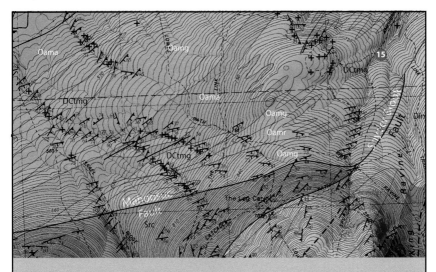

Src - Crawford Member -- Migmatitic gneiss with alternating layers of white quartz + feldspar and black biotite-rich schist

Oama - Ammonoosuc Volcanics -- A predominately dark green actinolite + biotite + garnet amphibolite facies metavolcanic tuff

Northwest portion of bedrock geologic map showing the symbols and abbreviations used to identify rock types. The color boxes below the map explain what Src and Oama are.

This map was created through the combined efforts of 33 geologists from Bates College in Lewiston, Maine, who investigated all outcrops of bedrock in the Presidential Range during the course of 14 field seasons. In order to find, measure, and describe each rock exposure, geologists hiked all the trails in the range as well as bushwacked up or down every ravine, ridge line, and brook. Some small rock samples were taken for microscopic analysis and radioactive age dating to determine the timing of geologic events. The abundant loose boulders were not mapped.

Cross Sections

The cross sections in the back pocket are labelled A-A′ and B-B′ and located on the map with thin white lines. The cross sections show the geology below the surface of the earth as well as the geology that has been eroded away when viewed as an imaginary vertical slice between each pair of points on the map. The arrangement of geologic units shown on the cross sections is determined by geometrically projecting the dips of features both below and above the ground surface. Today's skyline is represented by the change from faded (the above-ground eroded rocks) to solid colors (the geology below ground level).

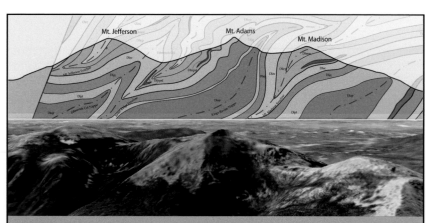

Portion of *cross section A-A′ through the Northern Presidentials showing the sub-surface geology below and eroded geology above the ground's surface. The Google Earth image on the bottom shows the location of the cross section through the high peaks of Mts. Jefferson, Adams, and Madison from west to east.*

Symbols on the Map

There are hundreds of symbols on the map that show the strike and dip, or orientation, of planar features that have been measured in rock outcrops. These represent sedimentary bedding surfaces or foliation planes defined by the parallel orientation of plate-like mica minerals that formed as rocks were deformed. Each symbol represents an exposure of rock where a geologist recorded a description of the rock and used a transit to measure the orientation of these features, expressed as values of strike and dip. The direction of strike is depicted by the long line of the symbol oriented as an azimuth, or bearing, with respect to north. The dip is symbolized by the short line or triangle, perpendicular to the strike line, labeled with a number that indicates the angle at which the plane descends into the earth (for example 24°). Other symbols with a "u-turn" arrow or half circle on the strike line tell whether the beds are upside-down, called "tops inverted,"

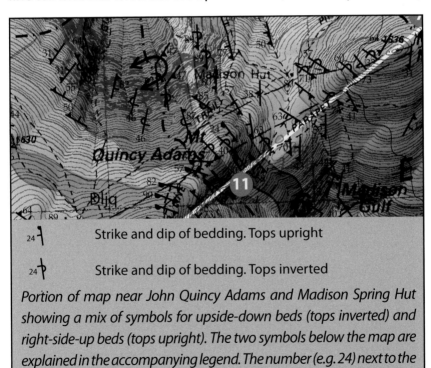

24⌐ Strike and dip of bedding. Tops upright

24ꝑ Strike and dip of bedding. Tops inverted

Portion of map near John Quincy Adams and Madison Spring Hut showing a mix of symbols for upside-down beds (tops inverted) and right-side-up beds (tops upright). The two symbols below the map are explained in the accompanying legend. The number (e.g. 24) next to the symbol shows the angle in degrees that the beds dip into the ground.

or right-side-up, called "tops upright," respectively. In the first instance, the rock layers were folded so that they were flipped over completely.

Faults and Folds

Faults and folds, which are large scale structures in the rocks, are also shown by a variety of line symbols explained in the legend. Both normal faults and thrust faults were mapped. In a normal fault, the block overlying the dipping fault, called the hanging wall, moves down the fault plane as it might under the influence of gravity. In a thrust fault, the hanging wall block moves up the fault plane against gravity due to compression by tectonic forces. Under some conditions, the rocks have been folded without fracturing along a fault plane. Folds that are bowed up are called anticlines, and those that are bowed down are called synclines. Some folds have been pushed over on their sides so that both limbs of the fold are nearly horizontal; these are called overturned folds. The Presidential Range has experienced six phases of folding and faulting. Each phase is called a "deformation"

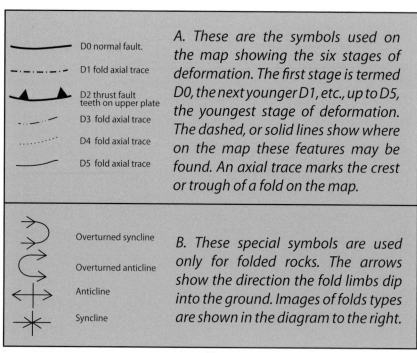

D0 normal fault.

D1 fold axial trace

D2 thrust fault
teeth on upper plate

D3 fold axial trace

D4 fold axial trace

D5 fold axial trace

A. These are the symbols used on the map showing the six stages of deformation. The first stage is termed D0, the next younger D1, etc., up to D5, the youngest stage of deformation. The dashed, or solid lines show where on the map these features may be found. An axial trace marks the crest or trough of a fold on the map.

Overturned syncline

Overturned anticline

Anticline

Syncline

B. These special symbols are used only for folded rocks. The arrows show the direction the fold limbs dip into the ground. Images of folds types are shown in the diagram to the right.

and abbreviated D#, with "#" being a number that indicates the relative age of the deforming events. For example, D0 represents a phase of normal faulting and the first and oldest deformation, and D5 represents the youngest phase of fold deformation.

Strike and dip

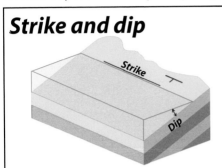

Strike is measured with respect to north, while dip is the angle that the rock layers descend into the earth. The symbol for strike and dip is plotted on the map.

Folds

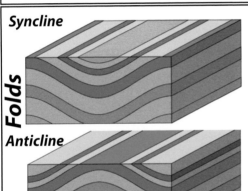

Syncline

In a syncline the layers dip towards each other forming a trough.

Anticline

An anticline is a fold where the layers dip away from each other forming an arch.

Faults

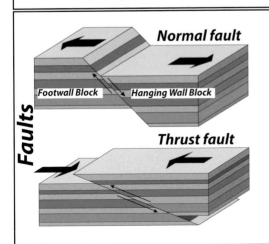

Normal fault

Footwall Block   Hanging Wall Block

A normal fault forms when the hanging wall block drops down the fault plane during tectonic extension.

Thrust fault

A thrust fault develops when overlying block moves up the fault plane during tectonic compression.

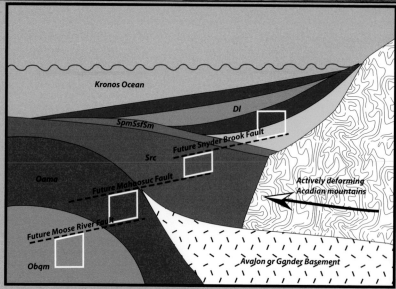

Kronos Ocean

Dl

SpmSsfSm

Future Snyder Brook Fault

Src

Future Mahoosuc Fault

Oama

Actively deforming
Acadian mountains

Future Moose River Fault

Obqm

Avalon or Gander Basement

408 Million Years Ago

When the Acadian mountains were moving northwest, sediment was deposited in front of them into the closing Kronos Ocean. The Avalon Plate is shown below the Acadian mountains and represents the "basement" upon which all the other rocks lie. The sediments of the Littleton Formation are shown in yellow, blue, and orange. These will eventually become the high peaks of the Presidential Range. Beneath these sediments are the Silurian Rangeley (green), Perry Mountain, Smalls Falls, and Madrid Formations (all three in red). These were deposited earlier into the Kronos Ocean and were covered by the Littleton Formation. The Ammonoosuc Volcanics (purple) and Oliverian Dome (light blue) erupted and intruded in the Ordovician during the Taconic Orogeny that formed Vermont. The Snyder Brook, Mahoosuc, and Moose River Faults that will form during the Acadian Orogeny are shown as dashed lines. The white boxes between the faults will merge through time as the faults move. The rocks in those boxes will become a single column of bedrock representing the geology seen today.

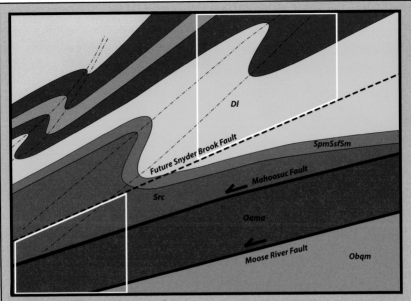

400 Million Years Ago

During this time, D0 faulting along the Mahoosuc and Moose River Faults developed. This is shown on the diagram above as the merging of three of the separated white outlined boxes in previous diagram bounded by the same faults. The faults are shown as heavy black lines with half arrows indicating fault motion. Evidence from the field suggests that these were normal faults that developed shortly after sedimentation depicted in the first diagram. D1 folding is also shown on this diagram in the Littleton, Madrid, Smalls Falls, Perry Mountain, and Rangeley Formations. This folding probably post-dated the D0 faulting. The land surface of the growing mountains at this time would have been about 10 kilometers above the D1 folds shown here. We do not know what geologic features existed in that upper 10 kilometers, as none of it remains due to hundreds of millions of years of erosion. All of these eroded rocks made their way to the Atlantic Ocean and were deposited as sediments, up to 15 kilometers in thickness, along the East Coast. In essence, the diagram above shows what was likely occurring 10 kilometers deep in the Earth during the beginning of the Acadian Orogeny.

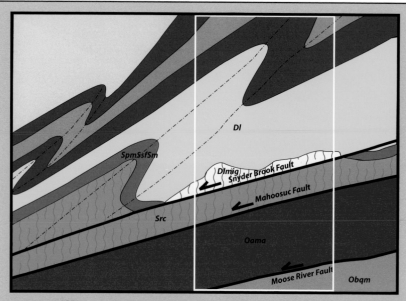

380 Million Years Ago

At this time, the D2 Snyder Brook Fault formed and widespread metamorphism developed. The Snyder Brook Fault cut through the Perry Mountain, Smalls Falls, and Madrid Formations (in red) and juxtaposed the cooler Littleton Formation (in yellow) against the hotter Rangeley Formation (in green). The heat within the Rangeley Formation was so great that some of it actually started to melt as temperatures approached 700° C, turning those portions into a metamorphic rock with igneous-like characteristics, called migmatite. It was so hot that portions of the Littleton Formation next to the Rangeley Formation partially melted (light yellow).

By this stage, all the once separated white outlined boxes have merged into a single column of bedrock. The mountains were likely at their highest in terms of elevation, probably about the size of the present Rocky Mountains. This diagram also represents the deepest the rocks of the Presidential Range were ever buried. The estimated depth of the geology shown in the diagram is approximately 13 kilometers below the land surface that existed in the Devonian time period.

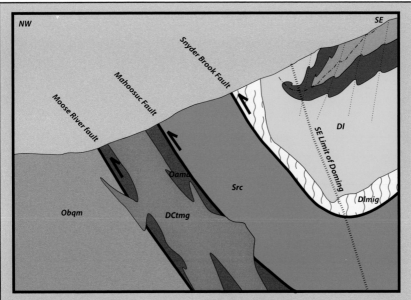

Today's Geology

This is a true-scale cross section from Randolph Valley to Mt. Adams with the Earth's surface represented by the transition from the colored geology to the gray region above. The 13 kilometers of overlying rock has been eroded away. The last stages of folding, D4, the culmination of the Acadian Orogeny, are shown as folds in the orange, blue, and yellow layers of the Littleton Formation. Notice also that on this present day cross section the regional dip is towards the right or southeast for the Oliverian Dome (light blue), Ammonoosuc Volcanics (purple), Rangeley Formation (green), and three faults. This change in dip resulted from a physical process akin to a "lava lamp," where the less dense Oliverian Dome rocks rose up as a solid, pushing aside the denser Ammonoosuc Volcanics. The rising Oliverian Dome tilted the once northwest dipping rocks to the southeast. This occurred around the same time as the D4 folds at the end of the Acadian Orogeny. The last gasp of the Acadian orogeny was the intrusion of a suite of igneous granites. These probably came from accumulations of the melted portions of the metamorphic rocks. The pink Bickford Granite (DCtmg) is shown above as it intruded into the already domed Ammonoosuc Volcanics.

Views From The Trail

Moose antler in Israel River tributary. Leave it as you see it.

D4 folds in a garnet layer within the Littleton Formation schists. These layers may have been garnet sands or thin volcanic deposits when originally formed.

Oliverian Domes and Ammonoosuc Volcanics

The oldest rocks in the Presidentials are found in the northwest corner of the map. They consist of a biotite quartz monzonite of the Oliverian Plutonic Series (Obqm) and part of the Jefferson Gneiss Dome. These are mantled by the next youngest rocks, Oama, Oamg, and Omar on the map or, collectively, the Ammonoosuc Volcanics. These are a mix of dark basaltic rocks with lighter fragments of what used to be rhyolite (Photo 1 on map and below).

The Oliverian and Ammonoosuc rocks are part of the 450 million year old Bronson Hill volcanic island arc that collided with what is now Vermont to form the Green Mountains during an earlier mountain building event called the Taconic Orogeny. At this point in time, none of the other rocks shown on the map existed. Metamorphism by the intense heat and pressure resulting from this and later collisions changed the volcanics into amphibolites; rocks rich in the black needle-like mineral amphibole. The Obqm gneiss was originally a lower density rock buried by more dense Oam Ammonoosuc Volcanics. This created an unstable situation with lighter rocks underlying heavier rocks. During later plate collisions, the Obqm rose up through the Oam and younger rocks as a flowing solid to make the broad Jefferson Dome, creating a more stable rock mass.

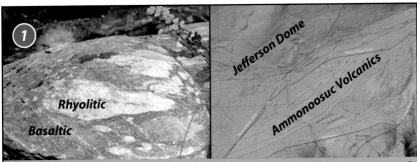

Photo 1 shows the dark basaltic and light rhyolitic portions of the Ammonoosuc Volcanics. A portion of the map showing the Jefferson Dome and Ammonoosuc Volcanics to the southeast.

Views From The Trail

Mts. Washington, Clay, and Jefferson from the Gulfside Trail. A snow patch is visible in the center of this photo taken in July.

Mt. Jefferson, Mt. Adams, and Mt. Madison, left to right, as seen from the headwall of the Great Gulf. Spaulding Lake lies in the bottom of this U-shaped glacial cirque which was carved by ice 20,000 years ago.

Silurian Formations

The sedimentary rock history for the rest of the Presidential Range begins with deposition of the Rangeley Formation (Sr on the map). This rock was deposited in the Early Silurian period, 430 million years ago, in the deep marine Kronos Ocean basin immediately east of the Bronson Hill volcanic arc. The Rangeley Formation is largely gneiss and had been extensively metamorphosed up to the point where it actually started to melt in places. Photo 2 shows an outcrop where the lighter quartz and feldspar rich layers are the now solidified, once melted, parts.

Rangeley Formation

The Rangeley gneisses also have blocks of different rock types embedded in them, ranging in size from centimeters (Photo 3) to meters (Photo 4). These formed by a combination of processes. First, earthquakes caused sub-marine landslides

The Silurian Rangeley Formation.

Photo 2 shows a typical example of the Rangeley migmatite where the dark regions are biotite-rich zones interlayered with lighter quartz and feldspar-rich zones that melted.

Photo 3 shows another common rock type in the Rangeley. The disc-shaped pod in the left center is composed of calcium-silicate minerals such as garnet, diopside, and plagioclase. It lies within the migmatite matrix.

Photo 4 shows an atypical outcrop containing large, 5-meter in length, blocks of dark amphibolite surrounded by light granite and then the swirly migmatite in both the foreground and background.

along normal faults; the Mahoosuc, Graham Trail, and Pinkham Notch normal faults shown on the map. These seismic events broke the Rangeley Formation into a disaggregated mix of blocks surrounded by a muddy matrix. Second, as the Rangeley Formation metamorphosed and experienced partial melting, fluids and magma moved through the rock, further breaking it up into what we see in the Presidential Range today. Some of the blocks are big enough to show on the map. For example, the calc-silicate granofels of Srcg and Sreg, rusty schists of Srcr, and amphibolites of Srea have been found on the flanks of Mt. Monroe, Mt. Eisenhower, and Mt. Clay, as well as down in the Route 16 Pinkham Notch valley at Emerald Pool.

Perry Mountain, Smalls Falls, & Madrid Formations

After deposition of the Rangeley Formation and throughout the remainder of the Silurian time period (to 410 million years ago), the Perry Mountain, Smalls Falls, and Madrid Formations were laid down in the ancient Kronos ocean basin. Each of these formations is quite thin, often discontinuous and composed of unique white quartzites (Spm), rusty schists (Ssf), and gray-green calcium-silicate granofels (Sm) (Photo 5).

The depositional setting for these formations is envisioned as a shrinking marine basin in which the geochemical environment became progressively more reducing as it was cut off from an oxygen supply. Subsequently the Kronos Ocean became a more open, oxygenated basin with good circulation. The Smalls Falls Formation is now weathering to a rusty-brown color, suggesting that it was oxygen-starved as a marine sediment. These characteristics result from the weathering of iron-bearing sulfide minerals like pyrite or pyrrhotite, where the iron is in the reduced chemical form. Atmospheric oxygen attacks these minerals resulting in iron-oxide minerals like hematite. The Madrid Formation is purple and green in color with a good deal of carbonate. At the time of deposition these rocks were in warm equatorial waters so a carbonate reef composed of limestone probably served as a sedimentary source for the Madrid Formation. This change from an oxygen-starved ocean basin to a more open

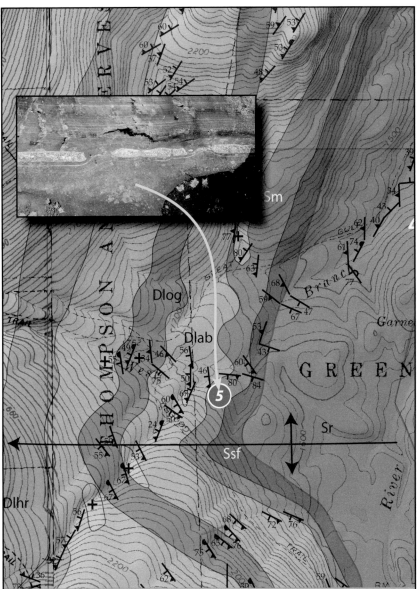

A portion of the map showing the lower elevations of Great Gulf and the West Branch of the Peabody River where excellent exposures of all the Silurian formations outcrop. Photo 5 shows an exposure of the Madrid Formation just above Long Island Rapids. This is a thinly laminated biotite and calcium silicate-rich rock type, a granofels, that is quite distinctive, but rare in the Presidential Range.

basin was caused by global plate interactions where some barrier to circulation opened up relatively quickly. These formations are quite distinctive in appearance, but generally difficult to find. The best places to see them are near Lakes of the Clouds, on Boott Spur, the base of the Lower Headwall at Tuckerman Ravine and, especially, along the West Branch of the Peabody River in Great Gulf just above Long Island Rapids.

Views From The Trail

The contact, or boundary, between the Madrid Formation and Littleton Formation is nicely exposed in the steep faces of the "Lower Headwall" of Tuckerman Ravine. The boundary is shown by the white line. This locality is below the main bowl of Tuckerman Ravine but above Hermit Lake. Here the Madrid Formation shows alternating layers of lighter calcium-silicate and plagioclase feldspar rich granofels and darker biotite-rich granofels. The Littleton Formation above is a massive schist without layering. Aaron is preparing to measure the contact.

Littleton Formation

The Littleton Formation was then deposited atop the Silurian Rangeley, Perry Mountain, Smalls Falls and Madrid Formations in the Early Devonian period, 409 million years ago. It was eroded and transported from the Avalon plate to the east. This sedimentation episode heralded the onset of the Acadian Orogeny that built the framework for today's Presidential Range. The Littleton Formation is made up of different combinations of what were once mud and sand deposited in the deep Kronos Ocean. These sediments were metamorphosed during the Acadian collision and are now schists and quartzites respectively. On the map, units shown in various shades of yellow, such as

Photographs of the Devonian Littleton Formation. In photo 6, the smooth, light gray, fine-grained quartzite (Q) grades, in the direction of the arrow, into the coarse-grained andalusite schist (S) to the right. The arrow points in the "topping" direction of the old marine sediment indicating that the now tilted layers get younger in the direction of the arrow. Another quartzite rests on top of the schist to the far right. Photo 7 shows thin, rhythmically bedded schist and quartzite east of the Mt. Madison summit cone. The latter is slightly indented as they weather faster than the schists.

Dlmj, Dlcp, and Dlab, are schist-rich with only 10-20% quartzite. Units that are blue, such as Dlog, Dlag, Dlirp, and Dlgg on the map, are quartzite-rich with less than 50% schist (Photo 6). The orange-colored units, such as Dlmm and Dlhr on the map, have roughly equal amounts of schist and quartzite layers interbedded on the centimeter scale (Photo 7).

Submarine Fans

The Littleton Formation was deposited as a series of overlapping submarine fans on the slope of the Kronos Ocean. As the name indicates, these underwater features have a fan-like shape and the sediment moves from the "handle" of the fan spreading toward its outer edge. Each fan has a feeder channel that is primarily filled with sands and extended downslope from the "handle." Sediments become progressively more mud-rich with increasing distance from the channels towards the edge of the fan. The massive schists that formed from these muds, like the Parapet near Star Lake or in Edmands Col (Dlec), were probably the distal (or outermost) edges of one such fan. The thin, evenly bedded muds and sands (schists and quartzites) exposed on Mt. Madison (Photo 7, Dlmm) and throughout Bigelow Lawn (Dlbl) were probably the mid section of a fan. The thick sands (quartzites) exposed on the shoulder of Sam Adams just above Storm Lake (Dlirp), along Osgood Ridge, and also just above the Alpine Garden (Dlag) on the Mt. Washington summit cone were probably the feeder channel to various fans. In these fans, muds or schists dominate. Muds interbedded with the sands (schists and quartzites) are the next most common, and sands (quartzites) are quite rare. The exact number and locations of fans that made up the Littleton Formation is unknown in part because of the subsequent complex deformation but also as a result of incomplete exposure.

The estimated total thickness of the entire Rangeley, Perry Mountain, Smalls Falls, Madrid, and Littleton Formations is 3.5 kilometers, but possibly much more as neither the base of the Rangeley Formation nor the top of the Littleton Formation has ever been identified.

Deformation of the Rocks

The Acadian collision began after the Littleton Formation was deposited in front of the advancing Avalon plate. There were six pulses of deformation. Some happened before, some during, and some at the end of this collision. Geologic features associated with this deformation have special symbols on the map and are labeled, from oldest to youngest, as D0, D1, D2, D3, D4, or D5.

D0 deformation is characterized by normal faults that predated the main collision. The Mahoosuc, Graham Trail, Moose River, and Pinkham Notch normal faults formed during this time, and represent earthquake-triggered slumps on the seafloor after deposition of the Rangeley and before or during deposition of the Littleton sedimentary rocks. The intervening Perry Mountain, Smalls Falls, and Madrid Formations were completely or partially cut out by the faulting. On the map, the truncation caused by the Graham Trail fault is seen on the Glen Boulder Trail below the actual boulder.

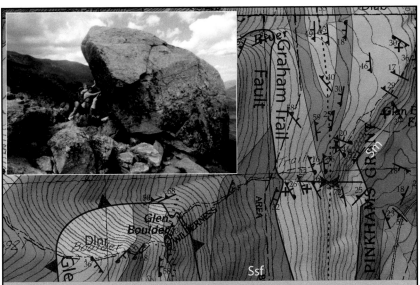

This is the portion of the map near Glen Boulder (inset photo) where the D0 Graham Trail Fault is well exposed. The fault cuts out the Madrid and Smalls Falls Formations and formed first in the six stages of deformation in the Presidential Range.

D1 Folding

D1 deformation is characterized by folds in the rock that formed 10 to 15 kilometers below the Earth's surface around 408 million years ago. At that depth, the rocks were warm, malleable and ductile, so that they "crumpled" in response to squeezing by plate collisions, rather than fracturing along faults. The overall geometry of folds can be described by two measures: the distance from one limb to another (the wavelength) and the distance or height from the trough to the peak (the amplitude). In the case of the D1 folds, wavelength is on the order of one kilometer and amplitude is about two kilometers. This is illustrated by the cross sections on the map, and in particular by section A-A' through the northern Presidential Range where three giant folds pointing east have been mapped. Each fold has a long right-side-up limb that gives way to a sharp hinge which in turn transitions into a shorter upside-down limb. Photos 8 and 9 show two D1 fold hinges on Osgood Ridge and along the Auto Road.

On the map, regions of upside-down (inverted) limbs are symbolized by "u-turn" dip arrows on the strike lines; conversely, regions of right-side-up (upright) limbs are symbolized by half circles on the strike lines. The best place to see examples of these features is below the summit of Mt. Washington along Chandler

D1 folds, Presidential Range.

Photo 8 shows a D1 fold on Osgood Ridge east of Mt. Madison. The red line traces the folded bedding. The rock is mostly quartzite with a few thin schist layers.

Photo 9 shows a D1 fold on the Auto Road at about 4,500 feet. The coarse-grained schist folds around the smoother quartzite as highlighted by the red line.

Ridge parallel to the Auto Road. The very top of Mt. Washington is composed of upside-down Littleton Formation. The rocks remain in this orientation until the "Cow Pasture" at 6,000 ft. where the first of two giant fold hinges are seen. From there down to Cragway Springs the rocks are all right-side-up. Further down the mountain, the second giant fold hinge is exposed near the Halfway House site. From there the rocks go through one more upside-down to right-side-up transition so that along Route 16 in Pinkham Notch the orientation is right-side-up again.

Greenough Springs D2 Fault

D2 deformation is characterized by the Greenough Springs Fault, which is seen in the center of the map. An abrupt break between the folded Littleton and Rangeley Formations occurs along the fault where D1 folds and the Madrid, Smalls Falls, and Perry Mountain Formations are all cut out and missing. The fault also marks a sharp transition in the degree of metamorphism, with the Rangeley Formation having been partially melted on one side of the fault, while the Littleton Formation, on the other side, was not melted as much. This is evidence that D2 faulting must postdate the partial melting and also be younger than the D0 normal faults. The Greenough Springs Fault formed as a thrust during the Acadian collision, but after the D1 folds. During

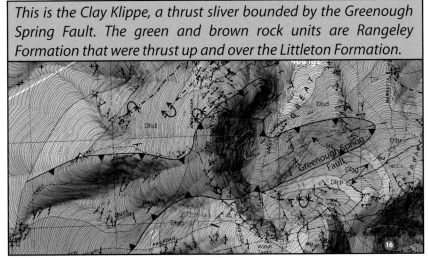

This is the Clay Klippe, a thrust sliver bounded by the Greenough Spring Fault. The green and brown rock units are Rangeley Formation that were thrust up and over the Littleton Formation.

thrusting, the older, deeper, and hotter Rangeley Formation was brought up over the younger, shallower, and cooler Littleton Formation.

Folding, Folding, and More Folding

D3, D4, and D5, the last three deformations related to the Acadian Orogeny, were a succession of fold events that marked the final compression recorded by the rocks. Evidence of D3 and D5 is not widespread and found only in the Great Gulf and Pinkham Notch regions respectively. D3 folds are shown with a dash–two dot line pattern on the map folding the Greenough Springs thrust. D5 folds are identified by a solid line pattern and are seen near the base of the Auto Road. D4 folding occurs throughout the Presidential Range and is observed on the centimeter to meter scale. Some of the best places to see the folds include the Cragway Springs hairpin corner on the Auto Road (Photo 10) and the south side of Mt. John Quincy Adams (Photo 11).

Photographs of D4 folding in the Presidential Range. Photo 10 is at Cragway Springs on the Auto Road. The folds have long west dipping limbs and shorter east dipping limbs. Photo 11 shows dark schists and light quartzites in a D4 fold on the south side of John Quincy Adams.

A few D4 folds are larger in size with wavelengths on the order of one to three kilometers. One of these is found along Chandler Ridge near Nelson Crag where a dome occurs like an upside-down bowl. Adjacent to it, near the three mile mark of the Auto Road, is a matching basin, looking like a right-side-up bowl. These folds are also seen on cross section B-B' where the D1 Tuckerman Ravine syncline is refolded by D4 folds.

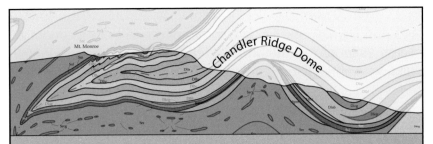

Map-scale D4 folds on cross section B-B' showing the Chandler Ridge Dome. On the cross section the layering is bent into an upside-down bowl and to the right of that fold is another, shaped like a bowl. An earlier D1 fold, the Tuckerman Ravine syncline, is seen below Mt. Monroe.

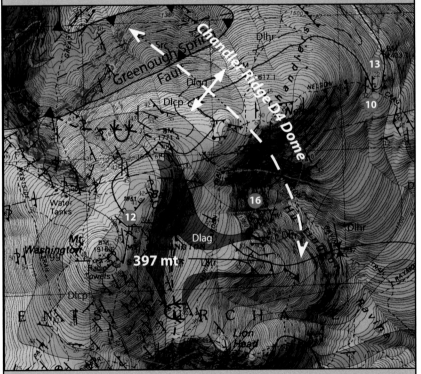

Map of the Chandler Ridge Dome, a large D4 fold shown in cross section in the upper illustration. The white dashed line shows the location of the crest of the dome and the arrows pointing away from the line show the dip of the dome flanks.

The D0 normal faults, D1 giant folds, D2 Greenough Springs fault and D3, D4, and D5 late folds collectively record about 40 million years of rock deformation during the Acadian mountain building events. Deformation started about 408 million years ago and ended 360 million years ago with the intrusion of granites that cross cut all the folds and faults.

Views From The Trail

Mt. Madison summit cone from the Gulfside Trail. Madison Spring Hut (AMC) is in the center of the photogaph. On the trail up Mt. Madison D4 folds deform a section of beds with tops inverted. In the foreground the Littleton Formation is dominated by beds with tops upright. In the saddle lies the axis of a large D1 fold.

New Minerals Grow

During the Acadian collision, metamorphism and deformation occurred simultaneously. The muds of the Littleton Formation were transformed from sedimentary shales into metamorphic schists, and in some places, gneisses, which are composed of new minerals. The sands changed into quartzites, but with little change to the overall rock mineralogy. The new minerals in the schists grew at geologic rates during metamorphism. Some of the common minerals that formed included thin, plate-like micas including both black biotite and clear muscovite, ruby-red garnet, and black tourmaline. Amber-brown, rectangular staurolite, pale-pink pencil-like andalusite, and fibrous white sillimanite are some of the less well-known, but nonetheless, important minerals that grew during this transformation.

Metamorphism occurred in a series of pulses, much like the episodic history of deformation described above. Some metamorphic events were extensive and some localized. The earliest metamorphism occurred during the D1 folding and is characterized by the mineral andalusite. It forms the knobby, centimeter or larger sized bumps that give the Littleton Formation schists their characteristic rough texture and fabric. Because crystal growth occurred during D1 deformation, andalusite often appears as aligned rods up to 10 cm in length. Sillimanite formed next through recrystallization of andalusite and looks like tiny bundles of microscopic, stiff, clear-to-white hair found within andalusite. This transformation happened during the partial melting that affected the Rangeley Formation during the end of D1 folding. The green unit Src on the map shows the extent of the partially melted rock called a migmatite. Muscovite formed many times during the metamorphism, both during and after D1 folding, but always before D4 and D5 deformation.

Temperature and Pressure Rise

The conditions of temperature and pressure that the rocks in the Presidential Range were exposed to during the Acadian collision can be determined by the minerals that formed during metamorphism. The occurrence of staurolite, andalusite, and sillimanite in the schists means that temperatures and pressures

Metamorphic rocks of the Littleton Formation. Photo 12 shows a schist with the mineral andalusite, an aluminosilicate composed of Al_2SiO_5. The minerals are four to six inches in length and aligned so that most of the crystals point down the rock face. This alignment occurred during D1 deformation.

The photo shows the entire metamorphic process as recorded in one crystal of andalusite. The rectangular four inch long mineral outlined in yellow in the photo is the former andalusite crystal. White sillimanite has completely replaced the andalusite and is clearly visible in its center outlined by the white line. Surrounding the sillimanite is a rim of muscovite (between the yellow and white lines) that replaced most, but not all, of the sillimanite.

reached as high as 500°-700° Celsius at 3,000-4,000 Atmospheres. This represents a dramatic change from the conditions that existed when the original sediments were muds on the Kronos Ocean bottom (25° Celsius at 1 Atmosphere). The increase in pressure resulted from burial by a mountain-sized stack of D1 folds and D2 fault slices as these sediments were caught in the collision between the Avalon and Laurentian plates. The increase in heat resulted from a steady rise in temperature as the rocks were deeply buried. Heat also came from molten rock magma and superheated geothermal fluids within the Acadian collision zone.

In order to be subjected to a pressure of 3,000-4,000 Atmospheres, the rocks of the Presidential Range would have had to be buried under an additional rock mass that was about 13 kilometers thick. This great thickness of overlying rock has long

Rocks: How hot? How deep?

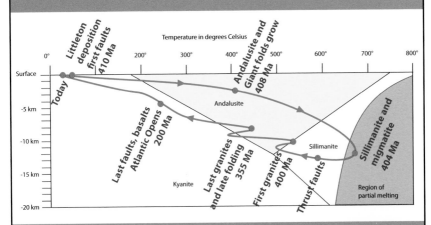

This graph shows temperature increasing from left to right, and depth in the earth increasing from top to bottom. The green line with red dots illustrates the history of temperature and depth conditions for the rocks in the Presidential Range. The blue writing at each dot describes the major geologic events and ages, in millions of years (Ma) during the formation of the range. For example, the red dot at the far right in the pink region represents when some of the rocks reached their maximum temperatures of about 700 ° Celsius, high enough so that these rocks began to melt. This occurred 404 million years ago as determined by radioactive age dating methods.

The regions of growth for the minerals andalusite, sillimanite, and kayanite are shown by the thin black lines. Andalusite, for example, only grows in schists when the temperatures and depths are within the yellow triangle labeled "Andalusite" on the graph. The rocks began as sediments on the ancient Kronos Ocean seafloor (410 Ma) and were buried during the plate tectonic collisions to maximum depths of up to 13 kilometers (404 Ma). Intrusions of granites caused short-lived increases in the temperature of the rocks (400 and 355 ma). The rocks slowly eroded until the opening of Pangea and the creation of the Atlantic Ocean when erosion sped up (200 Ma). Today, at the surface of the Presidential Range, rocks are now exposed that initially formed hundreds of millions of years ago as marine sediments.

How tall were the mountains?

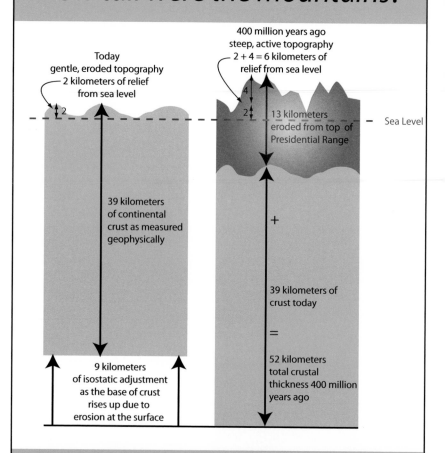

Today
gentle, eroded topography
2 kilometers of relief
from sea level

2

400 million years ago
steep, active topography
2 + 4 = 6 kilometers of
relief from sea level

4

2

13 kilometers
eroded from top of
Presidential Range

Sea Level

39 kilometers
of continental
crust as measured
geophysically

+

39 kilometers of
crust today

=

52 kilometers
total crustal
thickness 400 million
years ago

9 kilometers
of isostatic adjustment
as the base of crust
rises up due to
erosion at the surface

These two columns show the Presidential Range today on the left, and at its maximum height, about 400 million years ago on the right. Sea level is shown as the thin, blue-dashed horizontal line. Today we know from geophysical measurements that the continental crust in New England is 39 kilometers thick. The column on the right was made by adding back the 13 kilometers of rock that has eroded over the last 400 million years, giving a continental crust thickness of 52 kilometers. This extra mass would settle (via isostatic adjustment) by depressing into the Earth's fluid-like mantle resulting in an elevation of the ancient Presidential Range of 6 kilometers or 15,000 feet: as tall as the Rocky Mountains, but not as tall as the Himalayas.

Presidential Range skyline 400 million years ago. 6 kilometers above sea level

Presidential Range skyline today. 2 kilometers above sea level

This would be the view of the ancient Presidential Range from the west, near Lancaster, New Hampshire, 400 million years ago. The mountains would have been about 6 kilometers tall or about 15,000 feet above sea level and the topography would have been much more jagged and rough in the new growing mountains.

since weathered and eroded away over the last 360 million years. The products of this erosion are the deposits of sediment on the Atlantic continental shelf and slope that exist today.

Snow-white quartz lenses seen in places like Edmands Col and near Star Lake are another product of metamorphism in the Presidential Range. These are quite visible to the eye as they are so bright and white. During metamorphism, these lenses formed from fluids squeezed and heated out of the rocks through a dehydration process. The fluids were composed of water, and dissolved silica, fluorine, boron, and carbon dioxide. As they percolated through the rocks, most of these fluids escaped to the Earth's surface and became part of the atmosphere, but some, especially the most silica-rich, cooled to a solid during their passage upward through the Littleton Formation schists.

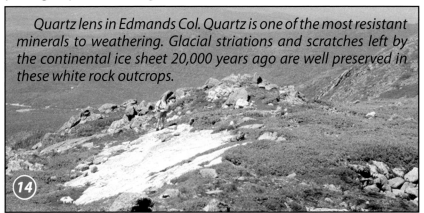

Quartz lens in Edmands Col. Quartz is one of the most resistant minerals to weathering. Glacial striations and scratches left by the continental ice sheet 20,000 years ago are well preserved in these white rock outcrops.

(14)

The famous "STOP" sign greeting hikers in the alpine zone. The weather is indeed challenging. Approaching thunderstorms, 100+ mile per hour winds, summer snow, horizontal rain, and slippery rocks are just as much part of being above treeline as are the excellent views, blue skies, well marked trails, and mountain huts. The Alpine Zone is very fragile so please stay on the marked trails when hiking through it and always camp below timberline.

Granites

There are only a small number of granites exposed in this part of the Granite State. During metamorphism, pre-existing rocks partially melted and formed migmatites. Enough molten rock pooled and accumulated to produce granites. Two of the largest granites of this type are exposed at Wildcat Ski Area and in Bigelow Lawn. Both have been dated at 401 and 399 million years old respectively, synchronous with the intense metamorphism during the Acadian collision. There are also dozens of smaller granitic bodies that occur as pods between 5 and 100 meters in length within the metamorphic rocks. Many of these are coarse-grained, some with crystals up to several centimeters in length. One such pod is exposed along the summit of Mt. Monroe, another near Slide Peak, and others along Cold Brook near the Town of Randolph.

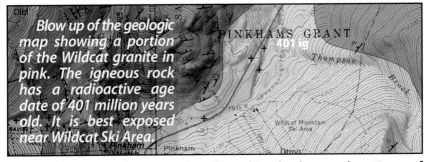

Blow up of the geologic map showing a portion of the Wildcat granite in pink. The igneous rock has a radioactive age date of 401 million years old. It is best exposed near Wildcat Ski Area.

There are three granites found in the lower elevations of the Presidential Range. These have been named the Peabody River, Bickford, and Bretton Woods granites. They all look very similar; white, small in grain size, and composed of the minerals quartz, feldspar, muscovite, and biotite. Photo 15 shows a typical granite exposure at Coldspur Ledges on Cold Brook, part of the Bickford granite. All three granites have been dated using radioactive methods and their ages cluster around 360 million years ago. This makes them a full 40 million years younger than the metamorphism and deformation described above. The likely cause of this period of igneous intrusion was the collapse of the ancestral Presidential Range after the tectonic stresses ceased. Once the stress that builds a mountain range and keeps it uplifted ceases, the mountains sag and decrease in elevation. As the mountaintops drop, the base of the Earth's crust rises up and heat from the underlying mantle causes the base of the crust to melt. This generates great volumes of new magma that rise up into the upper crust and cool to freeze as granites. These young granites cut across all the metamorphic rocks as well as the D1 folds and D2 faults. They are probably related to the late D5 and D4 folds and may have created the folds when the magma pushed its way up through the rocks.

The Bickford granite exposed at Coldspur Ledges on Cold Brook. This is one of three young granites that intruded about 360 million years ago at the end of the plate tectonic activity in the Presidential Range. Geologists Jesse and Matt are preparing to measure and describe the outcrop.

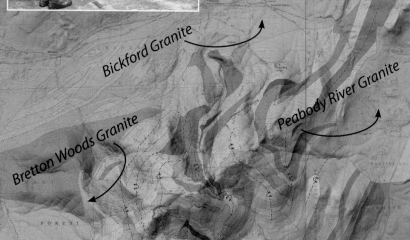

Bickford Granite

Peabody River Granite

Bretton Woods Granite

The three younger granites in the Presidential Range: The Bretton Woods, Bickford, and Peabody River granites. All of these granites are approximately 360 million years old and occupy the lower regions of the range, presumably because they eroded much more readily than the schists in the high peaks.

Basalts

Following the deformation, metamorphism, and granite intrusion of the protracted Acadian collision, extensive brittle deformation occurred as the supercontinent Pangea began to split apart. This rifting created the Atlantic Ocean and caused abundant fractures or cracks to form in all of the rocks throughout New England. This took place in the Triassic-Jurassic periods about 180 million years ago. There are cracks of this age on every rock face in the Presidential Range. The best places to see them are in the steep faces of the headwalls of King, Huntington, and Tuckerman Ravines. Look for vertical and horizontal cracks extending several meters in length along these rock faces. As these cracks formed, magma from the Earth's mantle intruded along some of them, injecting basalt dikes into the old metamorphic rocks and igneous granites.

A typical cross-cutting basalt dike occupying a crack in Pinnacle Gully, part of the Huntington Ravine headwall. There are many of these shown on the map and probably many more exist within the region but are buried by the forest and soil cover.

Portion of the map around Mt. Washington showing the basalt dikes in Huntington and Tuckerman Ravines as red lines.

Views From The Trail

A modern landslide on the west flank of Mt. Monroe. This slide formed in 1996 and exposed outcrops of the Rangeley Formation which afforded geologists a rare opportunity to study rocks that were, prior to the the slide, covered by soil and vegetation. Janna, who just scrambled up the slide collecting data along the way, admires the view. Landslides like these are part of the modern geologic story of the Presidential Range. Perhaps one landslide a year occurs in the area, often triggered by heavy rains on the steeper slopes.

Glaciers

The last geologic event to shape the Presidential Range was a succession of glaciations in the Quaternary period. The most recent glaciation culminated about 20,000 years ago as an ice sheet from Canada overrode Mt Washington and advanced as far south as Cape Cod, Massachusetts. It left scattered deposits in the Presidential Range notches as well as characteristic erosional landforms in the mountains, such as the glacial cirques of King, Huntington, and Tuckerman Ravines. Though the glaciers were an impressive erosional force modifying the existing landscape, they did not build the Presidential Range. As the bedrock geology reveals, all of the mountain building occurred 400 to 360 million years ago during the Acadian plate collision.

Tuckerman Ravine is a glacial cirque that formed about 20,000 years ago when an alpine glacier carved out the valley into this charactistic U-shaped cross sectional form. The talus in the left center of the photo is a landslide deposit from Lions Head. This rock fall post-dated the glaciation and represents the modern geologic activity in the Presidential Range.

Acknowledgements

Many thanks to the Bates College geology majors for their hard work and dedication to the geologic mapping. The last name of each student is located where they mapped during the year indicated. The author supervised and mapped throughout the entire area during the project. Support from the U.S. Geological Survey, New Hampshire Geological Survey, Randolph Mountain Club (RMC), Appalachian Mountain Club (AMC), Mt. Washington Auto Road, United States Forest Service, and Mount Washington Observatory is much appreciated. Many thanks to the reviewers, William Ash, Rick Chormann, Sarah Clemmitt, Michele Cormier, Michelle Cruz, Sarah Gallop, June Hammond Rowan, Doug Mayer, John Mudge, Peter Rowan, and David Wunsch. Thanks also to William Ash for the many InDesign tutorials. Lydia, you made it all possible. Thanks!

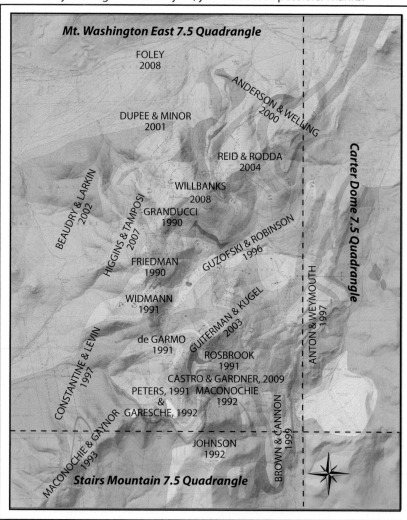

Mt. Washington East 7.5 Quadrangle

FOLEY
2008

ANDERSON & WELLING
2000

DUPEE & MINOR
2001

REID & RODDA
2004

WILLBANKS
2008

BEAUDRY & LARKIN
2002

HIGGINS & TAMPOSI
2007

GRANDUCCI
1990

GUZOFSKI & ROBINSON
1996

FRIEDMAN
1990

WIDMANN
1991

GUITERMAN & KUGEL
2003

de GARMO
1991

ROSBROOK
1991

CONSTANTINE & LEVIN
1997

ANTON & WEYMOUTH
1997

CASTRO & GARDNER, 2009
PETERS, 1991 MACONOCHIE
&   1992
GARESCHE, 1992

MACONOCHIE & GAYNOR
1993

BROWN & CANNON
1999

JOHNSON
1992

Stairs Mountain 7.5 Quadrangle

Carter Dome 7.5 Quadrangle

Photo 1. Oama: An amphibolite of the Ammonoosuc Volcanics, which before metamorphism was made up of basaltic and rhyolitic blocks. Located in Cold Brook above Cold Brook Falls at elevation 1,650 ft.

Photo 2. Src: Migmatite of the Crawford Member of the Rangeley Formation located at the falls where the Cabin Cascades Trail (RMC) crosses Cascade Brook at elevation 2,800 ft

Photo 3. Src: Calc-silicate lense within the migmatite of the Crawford Member of the Rangeley Formation. Located on Monroe Brook landslide at elevation 3,500 ft.

Photo 4. Srcg: Calc-silicate and amphibolite blocks within the Crawford Member migmatite, Rangeley Formation, located on Monroe Brook landslide at elevation 4,400 ft.

Photo 5. Sm: Madrid Formation calc-silicate granofels exposed in a northeast flowing side tributary to the West Branch of the Peabody River above Long Island Rapids at elevation 1,700 ft.

Photo 6. Dlgg: Great Gulf Member of the Littleton Formation showing well graded schists and quartzites on the winter cutoff of the Auto Road at elevation 4,500 ft.

Photo 7. Dlmm: Mt. Madison Member of the Littleton Formation showing thinly bedded schists and quartzites just east of the summit of Mt. Madison near the junction of the Watson Path (RMC) and Osgood Trail (USFS.)

Photo 8. Dlirp: Israel Ridge Path Member of the Littleton Formation showing massive quartzites in a D1 fold exposed on the Osgood Trail (USFS) just below the junction with the Daniel Webster Scout Trail (USFS) at elevation 4,500 ft.

Photo 9. Dlgg: Great Gulf Member of the Littleton Formation showing well graded schists and quartzites in a D1 fold exposed along the Auto Road at elevation 5,100 ft.

Photo 10. Dlhr: Huntington Ravine Member of the Littleton Formation with thinly bedded schists and quartzites in a D4 fold train exposed along the Auto Road at Cragway Springs corner elevation 4,800 ft.

Photo 11. Dljq: John Quincy Member of the Littleton Formation with thick schists and quartzites in a large D4 fold exposed on the southeast facing side of the lower, eastern summit of Mt. John Quincy Adams, elevation 5,300 ft.

Photo 12. Dlhr: Huntington Ravine Member of the Littleton Formation showing a massive schist with andalusite minerals aligned by D1 folding, 50 meters east of the Auto Road at elevation 6,050 ft.

Photo 13. Dlhr: Huntington Ravine Member of the Littleton Formation showing a schist with several andalusite minerals that have been replaced by sillimanite and muscovite, exposed on the inside part of Cragway Springs Corner on the Auto Road at elevation 4,825 ft.

Photo 14, Quartz pod: A snow-white quartz pod with micro-scale glacial striations oriented northwest-southeast, intruding into the Littleton Formation, and exposed in Edmands Col near the junction of the Randolph Path (RMC) and Castle Ravine Trail (RMC) at elevation 4,900 ft.

Photo 15, DCtmg: The Bickford Granite, a muscovite and biotite rich igneous rock with gently dipping sheeted fractures exposed at Coldspur Ledges near the junction of the Monoway (RMC) and Amphibrach (RMC) trails at elevation 2,200 ft.

Photo 16, Basalt Dike: A black, meter wide, basalt dike intruding into the Littleton Formation, exposed in Pinnacle Gully on the headwall of Huntington Ravine at elevation 5,100 ft.

Glossary of Geologic Terms

All definitions are modified from the Glossary of Geology provided online by the American Geological Institute
http://www.agiweb.org/pubs/glossary/index.html

Acadian Orogeny A middle Paleozoic tectonic event, especially in the northern Appalachians; it is named for Acadia, the old French name for the Canadian Maritime Provinces. The climax of the orogeny can be dated stratigraphically as early in the Late Devonian, but deformational, plutonic, and metamorphic events occurred over a more extended period. The Acadian is a consequence of convergent-margin tectonism and collision of exotic terranes with the eastern margin of North America. For example, the Avalon platform probably docked with Laurentia during the Acadian.

andalusite (an-da-lu'-site) A brown to red, orthorhombic mineral: Al2SiO5. Andalusite occurs in thick, elongate prisms in schists, gneisses, and hornfelses; it forms at medium temperatures and pressures of a regionally metamorphosed sequence and is characteristic of contact-metamorphosed argillaceous rocks.

anticline (an'-ti-cline) A fold, generally convex upward, whose core contains the stratigraphically older rocks. Ant: syncline.

Avalon The Avalon plate is a microcontinent that was sutured to eastern North America during the Devonian-age Acadian orogeny. Indications of the event, represented by radiometric dates ranging from slightly earlier to later, occur in accreted terranes along the southeastern edge of the Appalachian orogenic belt, and in rocks beneath the sediments of the Atlantic Coastal Plain as far southwest as Florida. It was named for the Avalon Peninsula, southeastern Newfoundland.

axial surface A surface that connects the hinge lines of the strata in a fold.

axial trace The intersection of the axial surface of a fold with the surface of the Earth or other given surface.

basalt (ba-salt', ba'-salt) A general term for dark-colored mafic igneous rocks, commonly extrusive but locally intrusive (e.g. as dikes), composed chiefly of calcic plagioclase and clinopyroxene; the fine-grained equivalent of gabbro.

biotite (bi'-o-tite) (a) A widely distributed and important rock-forming mineral of the mica group: K(Mg,Fe2+)3(Al,Fe3+)Si3O10(OH,F)2. It is generally black, dark brown, or dark green. It forms a constituent of crystalline rocks (either as an original crystal in igneous rocks of all kinds or a product of metamorphic origin in gneisses and schists) or a detrital constituent of sandstones and other sedimentary rocks. Biotite is useful in the potassium-argon method of age determination.

Bronson Hill The Bronson Hill terrane is an Ordovician volcanic arc, part of Gander, that collided with Laurentia in the Ordovician.

contact (con'-tact) n. A plane or irregular surface between two types or ages of rock; examples are faults, intrusive borders, bedding planes separating distinct strata, and unconformities.

deformation A general term for the process of folding, faulting, shearing, or fabric development of the rocks as a result of Earth stresses.

dike A tabular igneous intrusion that cuts across the bedding or foliation of the country rock. Also spelled: dyke.

dip n. The maximum angle that a structural surface, e.g. bedding or a fault plane, makes with the horizontal; measured perpendicular to the strike of the structure and in the vertical plane.

fault A discrete surface or zone of discrete surfaces separating two rock masses across which one mass has slid past the other.

feldspar (feld'-spar) (a) A group of abundant rock-forming minerals of general formula: $MAl(Si,Al)_3O_8$, where $M = K$, Na, Ca, Ba, Rb, Sr, or rarely Fe. Feldspars are the most widespread of any mineral group and constitute 60% of the Earth's crust; they occur as components of all kinds of rocks (crystalline schists, migmatites, gneisses, granites, most magmatic rocks) and as fissure minerals in clefts and druse minerals in cavities. Feldspars are usually white or nearly white and clear and translucent (they have no color of their own but are frequently colored by impurities).

fold n. A curve or bend of a planar structure such as rock strata, bedding planes, foliation, or cleavage. A fold is usually a product of deformation, although its definition is descriptive and not genetic and may include primary structures.

Gander The Gander plate is a microcontinent that was sutured to eastern North America during the Paleozoic. Gander crust underlies the Silurian and Devonian strata that were deformed in the Acadian orogeny. It was named for rocks in central Newfoundland.

garnet (gar'-net) A group of minerals of formula: $A_3B_2(SiO_4)_3$, where $A = Ca$, Mg, Fe^{2+}, or Mn^{2+}, and $B = Al$, Fe^{3+}, Mn^{3+}, V^{3+}, or Cr^{3+}. Garnet is a brittle and transparent to subtransparent mineral, having a vitreous luster, no cleavage, and a variety of colors, dark red being the most common. It occurs as an accessory mineral in a wide range of igneous rocks, but is most commonly found as distinctive euhedral cubic crystals in metamorphic rocks (gneiss, mica schist, marble); it may also be massive or granular. Garnet is used as a semiprecious stone and as an abrasive.

Gondwana (Gond-wa'-na) The late Paleozoic continent of the Southern Hemisphere. It was named for the Gondwana system of India, which has an age range from Carboniferous to Jurassic and contains glacial tillite in its lower part and coal measures higher up. Similar sequences of the same age are found in all the continents of the hemisphere; this similarity, along with much compelling evidence of other sorts, indicates that all these continents were once joined into a single larger mass. The preponderance of modern evidence indicates that the present continents are fragments that have been separated from each other by continental drift. The counterpart of Gondwana in the Northern Hemisphere was Laurasia; the supercontinent from which both were derived was Pangea.

gneiss A foliated rock formed by regional metamorphism, in which bands or lenticles of granular minerals alternate with bands or lenticles in which minerals having flaky (micas) or elongate prismatic habits predominate. Generally less than 50% of the minerals show preferred parallel orientation. Although a gneiss is commonly feldspar- and quartz-rich, the mineral composition is not an essential factor in its definition.

graded bedding A type of bedding in which each layer displays a gradual and progressive change in particle size, usually from coarse at the base of the bed to fine at the top. Grain sizes may reverse during metamorphism. It may form under conditions in which the velocity of the prevailing current declined in a gradual manner, as by deposition from a single short-lived turbidity current.

granite A plutonic rock in which quartz constitutes 10 to 50 percent of the felsic components and in which the alkali feldspar/total feldspar ratio is generally restricted to the range of 65 to 90 percent.

granofels (gran'-o-fels) A field name for a medium- to coarse-grained granoblastic metamorphic rock with little or no foliation or lineation.

igneous (ig'-ne-ous) Said of a rock or mineral that solidified from molten or partly molten material, i.e. from a magma; also, applied to processes leading to, related to, or resulting from the formation of such rocks. Igneous rocks constitute one of the three main classes into which rocks are divided, the others being metamorphic and sedimentary. Etymol: Latin "ignis", "fire".

intrusion The process of emplacement of magma in pre-existing rock; magmatic activity; also, the igneous rock mass so formed within the surrounding rock.

magma (mag'-ma) Naturally occurring molten or partially molten rock material, generated within the Earth and capable of intrusion and extrusion, from which igneous rocks are derived through solidification and related processes. It may or may not contain suspended solids (such as crystals and rock fragments) and/or gas phases.

Laurentia The protocontinent of the Northern Hemisphere, corresponding to Gondwana in the Southern Hemisphere, from which the present continents of the Northern Hemisphere have been derived by separation and continental drift. Collided with Avalon in the Acadian Orogeny.

metamorphism (met-a-mor'-phism) The mineralogical, chemical, and structural adjustment of solid rocks to physical and chemical conditions that have generally been imposed at depth, below the surface zones of weathering and cementation, and differ from the conditions under which the rocks in question originated.

mica (mi'-ca) A group of minerals of general formula: $(K,Na,Ca)(Mg,Fe,Li,Al)_{2-3}(OH,F)_2[(Si,Al)_4O_{10}]$. They include any mineral of the mica group: muscovite, biotite, lepidolite, phlogopite, zinnwaldite, roscoelite, paragonite, and sericite. Micas are characterized by low hardness and by perfect basal cleavage, readily splitting into thin, tough, somewhat elastic laminae or plates with a splendent pearly luster; and that range in color from colorless, silvery white, pale brown, or yellow to green or black. Micas are prominent rock-forming constituents of igneous and metamorphic rocks, and commonly occur as flakes, scales, or shreds. Sheet muscovite is used in electric insulators; ground mica in paint and as a dusting agent.

migmatite (mig'-ma-tite) A rock composed of igneous or igneous-appearing or metamorphic materials found in medium-grade to high-grade metamorphic areas, that is pervasively inhomogeneous on a macroscopic scale, one part being pale colored and consistently of quartzofeldspathic or feldspathic composition and the other dark and biotite-rich.

muscovite (mus'-co-vite) A mineral of the mica group: KAl2(Si3Al)O10(OH,F)2. It is colorless to yellowish or pale brown, and is a common mineral in gneisses and schists, in most acid igneous rocks (such as granites and pegmatites), and in many sedimentary rocks (esp. sandstones). Syn: white mica; potash mica; common mica; Muscovy glass; mirror stone.

normal fault A fault in which the hanging wall has moved downward relative to the footwall. The angle of the fault is usually 45-90°, and in most cases close to 60°.

orogeny (o-rog'-e-ny) Literally, the process of formation of mountains. Orogeny is the process by which structures within fold-belt mountainous areas were formed, including thrusting, folding, and faulting in the outer and higher layers, and plastic folding, metamorphism, and plutonism in the inner and deeper layers.

Pangea (Pan-ge'-a) A supercontinent that existed from about 300 to about 200 Ma ago and included most of the continental crust of the Earth, from which the present continents were derived by fragmentation and continental drift. During an intermediate stage of the fragmentation, between the existence of Pangea and that of the present continents, Pangea is believed to have split into two large fragments, Laurasia on the north and Gondwana on the south. The proto-ocean around Pangea has been termed Panthalassa.

pluton (plu'-ton) A deep-seated igneous intrusion.

Radioactive Age Dating Calculating an age in years for geologic materials by measuring the presence of a short-lived radioactive element (e.g., carbon-14) or by measuring the presence of a long-lived radioactive element plus its decay product (e.g., potassium-40/argon-40). The term applies to all methods of age determination based on nuclear decay of naturally occurring radioactive isotopes.

reverse fault A fault on which the hanging wall has moved upward relative to the footwall. The dip of the fault is usually greater than 45°.

schist A strongly foliated crystalline rock, formed by dynamic metamorphism, that can be readily split into thin flakes or slabs because of the well-developed parallelism of more than 50% of the minerals present, particularly the micas. The mineral composition is not an essential factor in its definition unless specifically included in the rock name (e.g., quartz-muscovite schist). Varieties may also be based on general composition (e.g., calc-silicate schist, amphibole schist) or on texture (e.g., spotted schist).

sedimentary rock A rock resulting from the consolidation of loose sediment that has accumulated in layers; e.g. a clastic rock (such as conglomerate or tillite) consisting of mechanically formed fragments of older rock transported from its source and deposited in water or from air or ice; or a chemical rock (such as rock salt or gypsum) formed by precipitation from solution; or an organic rock (such as certain limestones) consisting of the remains or secretions of plants and animals.

sillimanite (sil-li'-man-ite) A brown, gray, pale-green, or white orthorhombic mineral: Al2SiO5. Sillimanite occurs in long, slender, needlelike crystals often found in wisplike or fibrous aggregates in schists and gneisses; it forms at the highest temperatures and pressures of a regionally metamorphosed sequence and is characteristic of the innermost zone of contact-metamorphosed sediments.

staurolite (stau'-ro-lite) A dark reddish brown, blackish brown, yellowish brown, or blue mineral: (Fe,Mg)4Al17(Si,Al)8O45(OH)3. Twinned crystals often resemble a cross (six-sided prisms intersecting at 90° and 60°.) It is a common constituent in rocks such as mica schists and gneisses that have undergone medium-grade metamorphism.

striation (stri-a'-tion) One of multiple scratches or minute lines, generally parallel, inscribed on a rock surface by a geologic agent, e.g., glaciers (glacial striation), streams (cf: drag mark), or faulting (cf: slickenside.)

strike n. The direction or trend taken by a structural surface, e.g. a bedding or fault plane, as it intersects the horizontal.

subduction (sub-duc'-tion) The process of one lithospheric plate descending beneath another.

subduction zone A long, narrow belt in which subduction takes place, e.g. along the Peru-Chile Trench or in the volcanic arc belts of the western Pacific Ocean.

syncline (syn'-cline) A fold of which the core contains the stratigraphically younger rocks; it is generally concave upward.

thrust fault A fault with a dip of 45° or less over much of its extent, on which the hanging wall has moved upward relative to the footwall.

quartz Crystalline silica, an important rock-forming mineral: SiO2. It is, next to feldspar, the commonest mineral, occurring either in transparent hexagonal crystals (colorless, or colored by impurities) or in crystalline or cryptocrystalline masses. Quartz forms the major proportion of most sands, and has a widespread distribution in igneous (esp. granitic), metamorphic, and sedimentary rocks.

quartzite The term is also used for a metamorphic rock produced by recrystallization of a sandstone.

quartz monzonite A granitic rock in which quartz comprises 10-50% of the felsic constituents, and in which the alkali feldspar/total feldspar ratio is between 35% and 65%. With an increase in plagioclase and dark minerals, it grades into granodiorite, and with more alkali feldspar, into a granite.

vein A mineral (commonly quartz) filling of a fault or other fracture in a host rock, in tabular or sheetlike form, often with associated replacement of the host rock.

Recommended Reading/Viewing

New Hampshire Geological Survey
The bedrock geologic map of New Hampshire and many other excellent products about New Hampshire geology are available at: http://des.nh.gov/organization/commissioner/pip/publications/geologic/index.htm

Lithotectonic Map of the Appalachian Orogen, Canada-United States of America
Hibbard, J P; van Staal, C R; Rankin, D W; Williams, H. Geological Survey of Canada, "A" Series Map 2096A, 2006.

Paleomap Project, Christopher R. Scotese
http://www.scotese.com/ Excellent illustrations of plate tectonic movements through geologic time.

Earth: Portrait of a Planet
Second Edition, Stephen Marshak, 2005, University of Illinois. A great introductory geology textbook used by the author in his Bates College classes.

Welcome to webGeology
Excellent introductory geology on the web, with animations from the University of Tromsø, Norway, http://ansatte.uit.no/kku000/webgeology/

Maine Geological Survey
Great source of bedrock and surficial geologic maps of Maine. http://www.maine.gov/doc/nrimc/mgs/mgs.htm

Randolph Mountain Club
Great information on hiking trails and cabins in the Presidential Range. http://www.randolphmountainclub.org/

Appalachian Mountain Club
Source for a wide variety of recreational activities in the White National Forest. http://www.outdoors.org/

The Glossary of Geology
Available online through the American Geological Institute web site. http://www.agiweb.org/pubs/glossary/index.html

United States Geological Survey
Source for all types of geologic information, http://www.usgs.gov/

Notes

Notes

Notes

About the author:

J. Dykstra Eusden is Professor of Geology at Bates College, in Lewiston,

Maine. He received his B.S. from Bates College, M.S. from the University of New Hampshire, and Ph.D. from Dartmouth College. He teaches courses on tectonics and bedrock geology including "Field Geology in Maine" and "Geology of the Maine Coast by Sea Kayak". His research includes studies of ancient Appalachian tectonics and the active tectonics of New Zealand.